SONGS

of

STEPHEN FOSTER

STEPHEN COLLINS FOSTER
1826—1864

SONGS

of
STEPHEN FOSTER

Prepared for
SCHOOLS AND GENERAL USE

EDITED AND ARRANGED BY
WILL EARHART
Director of Music in the Pittsburgh Public Schools
AND
EDWARD B. BIRGE
Professor of Music, Indiana University

PUBLISHED BY THE
UNIVERSITY OF PITTSBURGH PRESS
1941

FOSTER HALL, INDIANAPOLIS, INDIANA

THE SONGS in this book and the greater part of the knowledge we now have of Stephen Foster's life and work have become available largely through the efforts of Josiah Kirby Lilly, of Indianapolis, Indiana. His fondness for the melodies of Stephen Foster led him to search for first editions of these songs, and then for portraits of Foster, and for information that would throw increasing light on the composer's life. A small building erected on his estate to house a pipe organ was named Foster Hall, and from 1931 to 1937 it became a fascinating treasure house of all things pertaining to Stephen Foster. In 1937 these things were given by Mr. Lilly to the "people of the United States," and they are enshrined in the Stephen Collins Foster Memorial, located on the University of Pittsburgh campus in the city of the composer's birth.

This collection of Foster songs is here presented for the second time. It first appeared in the Foster Hall edition published in 1934 by Mr. Lilly, who has since transferred publication rights to the University of Pittsburgh.

Manufactured in U. S. A.
Copyright 1934 by Josiah K. Lilly—Copyright 1938 by University of Pittsburgh
University of Pittsburgh Edition printed 1938—Reprinted 1939, 1940 and 1941

CONTENTS

STEPHEN C. FOSTER MEMORIAL
University of Pittsburgh, Pittsburgh, Pennsylvania

FOREWORD

AMERICAN CHILDREN are familiar with some of the best known songs of Stephen Foster, and they will find in the pages of this book many more which they will enjoy learning and singing. The songs are simple and lovable, and they belong to the whole world; for all hearts are alike in feeling tenderness, merriment, joy, sympathy, and love of home, and must have some beautiful way of expressing these feelings, such as we find in song.

But sometimes we forget the giver in the gift. We have accepted these songs as belonging to us; let us not forget the composer, who also belongs to us, and whose simple and kindly nature is so beautifully revealed in his music.

Stephen Collins Foster was born in Pittsburgh, Pennsylvania, on July 4, 1826, when it was a small town. On the day he was born two great Americans died: John Adams and Thomas Jefferson, second and third presidents of the United States. Stephen began to compose music in his early teens—his father wrote, when he was a youth, of "his strange talent for music"—but the great part of his composing was done between 1846 and 1864. He was only thirty-seven years old when he died.

This collection contains forty-one songs, selected from the two hundred or more compositions which he wrote. The best of these songs, perhaps ten or twelve in number, have outlived all exigency of time and circumstance and have joined those other ageless examples of art which only genius can produce.

The music of this collection has been taken directly from the first published editions, without alteration except a few corrections in wording, spelling and punctuation, as well as changes in key in certain songs to bring them within the range of youthful voices, and some rearrangement of voice lines in the choruses to conform to modern printing.

HOW TO SING THE SONGS

In singing the songs questions of style may become puzzling. A few suggestions may be helpful.

All the songs, like folk songs in general, are so sincere and heartfelt that any artificial sentiment in singing them would be unworthy. Your own taste will probably be a sufficient guide in this matter. *Old Folks at Home* is so deeply earnest in quality that no one would wish to sing it otherwise than simply and beautifully. On the other hand, some of the rollicking minstrel songs, such as *Camptown Races*, might tempt the singers to declaim and shout until good singing tone and musical charm would be lost. This opposite kind of error may be avoided by taking care to make every tone *sing to its very end*, no matter how energetically the tone is attacked at its beginning. The *ringing* quality should not drop out of the voice in singing, for instance, "De Camptown ladies sing dis song." The flat, toneless voice that would result is not a singing voice, even if it is a speaking voice.

When there is a long tone at the end of a phrase, as in every fourth measure of *Old Folks at Home*, it should be held its full length, and the measure should be completed. The tone should be held, too, *as though the singer liked it*, and this can be accomplished if the singer does something with the tone to make it interesting. Exceedingly slight fluctuations in power—an almost imperceptible swell, or a little decrease in power, or, more rarely, even a little increase, as though one were *growing into* the next phrase—will prevent those awkward, empty moments that sometimes are permitted to occur between phrases. Of course, no one who feels right about it will let the music die at any point.

Finally, most songs should not be held to a rigid *tempo*, such as a band uses for marching. This does not mean that notes should not receive the current number of beats, but it does mean that the beats are not all of the same speed. In *Old Folks at Home*, for instance, if you let the voice and words move naturally, you will find that the last two beats of the first measure tend to move a little more deliberately (possibly because so many words occur on them) and the first two beats of the second measure tend to move a little more lightly. Then the last two beats of the second measure tend to hold back slightly. It would be a pity to exaggerate these liberties; but it would be a greater pity to force the song along on a rigid mechanical beat. Stephen Foster was a sensitive soul, and he wrote for that most sensitive of musical agencies, the voice.

THE EDITORS

7

SUGGESTIONS
FOR ARRANGEMENT OF VOICES

ANGELINA BAKER

The verses of this song may be sung by a solo voice or by equal voices in unison; the *Chorus* by all, in four parts, or, if voices for that are not available, in unison.

BEAUTIFUL CHILD OF SONG

Both the one-part and the two-part sections will be found best adapted to treble voices only. Solo voices, or equal voices in unison, may be used.

BEAUTIFUL DREAMER

A solo voice might well sing the first eight measures of this song; a number of voices sing the next four measures in unison; the solo voice then sings four measures; and all in unison complete the verse. Or it may be sung in unison throughout, each singer omitting notes that are not in easy range.

CAMPTOWN RACES

In this song either one voice or a group of equal voices may sing the solo phrases, but all should sing the chorus response, "*Doo-dah!*" If voices for part-singing are not available, the *Chorus* may be sung, though less effectively, in unison.

COME WHERE MY LOVE
LIES DREAMING

This song was intended to be sung as a quartette, but is effective with many voices on a part, if the tone is not allowed to become too robust. Alternations of quartette and chorus, prevailingly in eight-measure sections, will also be found effective. The final four measures afford excellent play for the entire chorus.

COME WITH THY SWEET
VOICE AGAIN

This song is practically limited to treble voices, except when adult voices are present. The first eight measures might be taken *solo;* the next four, unison; the next three (to the two parts), *solo;* the next five, duet or semi-chorus (in two parts); the last four, two-part chorus. Or a solo voice on each part, or many treble voices on each part, might be adopted throughout the entire song.

DOLLY DAY

Any solo voice, or equal voices in unison, might sing the verse of this song, and all sing the four-part *Chorus.* Or the verse might be divided equally (eight measures each) between two solo voices, or between two groups singing unisonally, and the *Chorus* then be sung by all together. If voices for the harmonic parts are not available, the *Chorus* may be sung by all, in unison.

DOWN AMONG THE
CANE BRAKES

The verses may be sung by a solo voice, by different solo voices, or by equal voices in unison, perhaps changing groups for different verses. The *Chorus,* if not done *tutti,* with all parts, may be varied by having its first four measures sung by a solo voice or in unison by a few voices, and its last two measures (of voice) sung by all, in unison.

ELLEN BAYNE

The verses may be sung by a solo voice, or by treble voices in unison; the *Chorus* as a duet, or by a two-part chorus of treble voices. Unless changed voices can sing a high E easily they can not be used effectively.

FAIRY BELLE

The two parts for the verses may be sung as a duet, or by a treble-voice chorus in two parts. If four parts are not available for the *Chorus,* the first four measures of it would better be sung by a solo voice or by a few soprano voices in unison, the next four measures by full two-part chorus of treble voices.

FAREWELL, MY LILLY DEAR

A solo voice, or equal voices in unison, may sing the verses of this song. If the two-part *Chorus* is repeated, the repetition should be *pianissimo.* Such repetition will lose in effect if done after every verse. If basses are present they may easily join in the *Chorus* by singing, in the rhythm of the treble voices, the C's, G's, and F's of the piano left-hand part.

GENTLE ANNIE

An effective way of singing this song would be to have a solo voice sing the verses; several or all soprano voices sing the first four measures of the *Chorus;* the solo voice or a few treble voices sing the remaining four measures. Or the entire song may be sung by all voices in unison, so far as the range is adapted to individual voices.

GLENDY BURK

For the verses, a male voice, or several male voices in unison, if available, should be used. All should join in the *Chorus.*

HAPPY HOURS AT HOME

The verses will probably be most effective if sung by a number of voices in unison. In the *Chorus,* the tenor *obbligato* is essential only in the second and third measures, where the range is fortunately not extreme.

HARD TIMES COME AGAIN NO MORE

The verses of this song are most effective if treated solo-wise, by either a baritone voice (preferably) or by mezzo-soprano. It may nevertheless be sung very effectively in unison, preferably by male voices. The *Chorus* may be sung by all in unison, if parts are not available, or as printed, since both of these forms were provided in the original edition.

THE HOUR FOR THEE AND ME

This song may be sung as a duet or as a two-part chorus throughout.

JEANIE WITH THE
LIGHT BROWN HAIR

This song may be sung throughout by a solo voice or by treble voices in unison; or these ways might be alternated on successive verses. Another possibility would be to use a solo voice on the first eight measures, then voices in unison to the end. A solo voice would better, in any case, sing the cadenza after the hold (—), on the word "Oh," any other voices that are being employed then joining on the word "I."

KATY BELL

The verses may be sung by all or a number of sopranos in unison, or by a solo voice. The *Chorus* may be sung in parts, or, if only treble voices are available, it may be sung by all of these in unison.

LAURA LEE

All voices may sing in unison throughout, in this song. Individual singers may be obliged to omit notes of extreme range here and there.

MASSA'S IN DE COLD GROUND

The compass of this song permits of its being sung by almost all voices. The verses may be sung by either a solo treble or a baritone voice, or by a group of either of such voices in unison. Or the first eight measures could be sung by the lower of these voices, the higher might join in the next eight. If four parts, mixed voices, are available, tenors and sopranos should sing the upper part in the *Chorus*, altos and basses the lower part. Or, again, either male voices or treble voices could sing the entire song alone; and it might be well to change from one to the other for some one stanza.

MY BRUDDER GUM

If a tenor singer is available the verses may best be done by that voice, solo. Treble voices in unison will also be effective. If a balanced four-part chorus is not available, the *Chorus* may be sung in unison by all voices, each singer omitting notes that are outside a comfortable range.

MY OLD KENTUCKY HOME

Treble voices in unison may most effectively sing the verses of this song. If the *Chorus* also must be sung in unison, a small number of voices only should sing the verses.

NELL AND I

The one-part sections may be sung by a solo voice or by equal voices in unison; the two-part sections as duet or as two-part chorus or semi-chorus. If four parts, mixed voices, are not available for the close, that section may be sung in unison by all voices, so far as individual voice-ranges permit.

NELLY BLY

The verses may be sung optionally by a treble or by a baritone voice, or by a group of either of such voices, in unison. The chorus may be sung by all in unison, or in two parts. In the latter case, tenors and baritones, if present, should join, respectively, the first soprano and the second soprano part.

NELLY WAS A LADY

If voices for four-part singing in the *Chorus* are not available, the verses should be sung by a solo voice or by a limited number of voices in unison, in order to strengthen the *Chorus* by the addition of a number of voices. Otherwise, the verses may be sung by all, or by all equal voices, in unison.

OH! BOYS, CARRY ME 'LONG

For the verses of this song a solo baritone, or male voices in unison, will be found preferable, but good effect may be obtained with other voices. If the *Chorus* must be sung unisonally, some voices should be held in reserve and added only on the *Chorus*.

OH! SUSANNA

If tenor voices are available, the verses may well be taken as tenor solo or by tenors in unison. Treble voices will prove very effective, however. If the *Chorus* must be sung by treble voices in unison, only part of those present should sing the verses.

OLD BLACK JOE

The verses may be sung either by a solo, baritone or treble, or by a group of either kind, singing in unison. The *Chorus*, if basses are lacking, may be sung in two-parts, treble voices, or by all voices in unison on the melody.

OLD DOG TRAY

Any group of equal voices will be found effective for singing the verses of this song; or they may be sung with one or another solo voice. The *Chorus* is effective if sung in unison by equal voices, or in unison and octaves by unequal voices.

OLD FOLKS AT HOME

Either a solo voice, if an excellent one is available, or a number of voices in unison, may sing the verses. Since no parts are added in the *Chorus*, many voices should be held in reserve, to join at this point.

OLD MEMORIES

Treble voices only, in unison throughout, will be found most effective for this song. It may be varied, however, by using a solo voice for one verse, and voices in unison for the next. A further possibility is to use second soprano voices in the first eight measures, first soprano voices in the next eight, and either all, or the second sopranos alone, in the concluding section.

OLD UNCLE NED

Treble voices may sing the melody throughout, except that some low voices will need to be selected to sing the descending bass motive in the ninth measure of the vocal part.

OPEN THY LATTICE, LOVE

Treble voices only, except in case of adult choruses, can be used effectively. First sopranos only, in unison, should sing the first half, second sopranos and altos adding the lower part only, in the second half.

OUR BRIGHT SUMMER DAYS ARE GONE

The verses, one or all, may be taken most effectively by either a baritone or treble voice, solo, or by treble voices in unison. All voices, equal or unequal, may join in the *Chorus.*

PARTHENIA TO INGOMAR

In this song, treble voices in unison will be found superior to any solo voice that is likely to be available, for considerable depth and weight of tone are needed. The first stanza might, however, be assigned to only part of the voices, all joining on the second stanza.

RING DE BANJO

Soprano voices can sing the verses of this song acceptably. They should do so, in unison. The *Chorus,* should changed boys' voices not be available, may be sung in unison by all treble voices, but some of these may have to omit occasional high tones.

SOME FOLKS

A solo voice, either treble or baritone, a group of voices of either kind, or both voices or groups together, may sing the verses. In the *Chorus* the lower voices should transpose the one high F to a lower octave.

SUMMER LONGINGS

Both changed and unchanged voices may sing in unison and octaves in this song without bad effect.

SWEETLY SHE SLEEPS, MY ALICE FAIR

It may be well in this song to divide the class into high and *mezzo* voice-parts. The *mezzo* voices would then sing the first eight measures, the high voices the next eight, and all would sing the final eight. The plan would be followed in both verses.

UNDER THE WILLOW SHE'S SLEEPING

In this song all treble voices of proper compass may sing the verse in unison. If bass voices are lacking, the *Chorus* may be sung by using the two upper parts only. In this case, however, the verse should be sung by not more than half the voices that participate in the *Chorus.*

THE WHITE COTTAGE

The Birthplace of Stephen Foster, July 4, 1826
Lawrenceville, Pennsylvania (now a part of Pittsburgh)

MY OLD KENTUCKY HOME, GOOD NICHT

FOSTER'S PLANTATION MELODIES

Nº 20

As Sung by

Christy's Minstrels

Nº 18. FAREWELL MY LILLY DEAR.
Nº 19. MASSA'S IN THE COLD GROUND.

Written and Composed by

STEPHEN C. FOSTER.

25ª nett.

NEW YORK
Published by FIRTH, POND & CO. 1 Franklin Square,

Pittsburgh,
H. KLEBER.

Cleveland,
HOLBROOK & LONG.

St Louis.
BALMER & WEBER.

Entered according to Act of Congress A.D. 1853 by Firth Pond & Cº in the Clerks Office of the Dist. Court of the South. Dist. of N.York.

MY OLD KENTUCKY HOME
First Edition

Waketurn

MY OLD KENTUCKY HOME, GOOD-NIGHT!

Published by Firth, Pond & Co., 1853.

According to a tradition which has not been verified, this famous song was written in Bardstown, Kentucky, at "Federal Hill," the home of Stephen Foster's relatives, the Rowans. It is said that Stephen and his wife were visiting their cousins in the summer of 1852. *My Old Kentucky Home* is supposed to have been inspired by the beauties of the Kentucky country-side.

"Federal Hill" is now a state shrine, and many thousands of persons come every year from every state in the Union to see it.

My Old Kentucky Home was made the official state song by act of the Kentucky legislature in 1928.

Harold Vincent Milligan comments as follows on *My Old Kentucky Home:*

"The song rings true and expresses an emotion deep-rooted in the human soul. Its only rival in the affectionate esteem of the multitudes is *Old Folks at Home* which it closely resembles in spirit. Both songs sing of loneliness and longing, of yearning over the happiness of days gone by."

corn-top's ripe and the mead-ow's in the bloom, While the birds make music all the day. The

young folks roll on the lit-tle cab-in floor, All mer-ry, all hap-py and bright: By'n

by Hard Times comes a-knock-ing at the door, Then my old Ken-tuck-y Home, Good-night!

CHORUS

Weep no more my la-dy, Oh! weep no more to-day! We will

sing one song for the old Ken-tuck-y Home, For the old Ken-tuck-y Home, far- a -way.

2d V. They hunt no more for the pos-sum and the coon On the meadow, the hill and the shore, They

sing no more by the glim-mer of the moon, On the bench by the old cab-in door. The

day goes by like a shad-ow o'er the heart, With sor-row where all was de-light: The

time has come when the dark-ies have to part, Then my old Ken-tuck-y Home, good-night! Chorus

3d V. The head must bow and the back will have to bend, Wher-ev-er the dark-ey may go: A

few more days. and the trou-ble all will end In the field where the sug-ar-canes grow. A

few more days for to tote the wea-ry load, No mat-ter 'twill nev-er be light, A

few more days till we tot-ter on the road, Then my old Ken-tuck-y Home, good-night! Chorus

[14]

COME WHERE MY LOVE LIES DREAMING

QUARTETTE

Published by Firth, Pond & Co., 1855.

A serenade that has long been popular. This song was played at Stephen's funeral by the musicians of Pittsburgh.

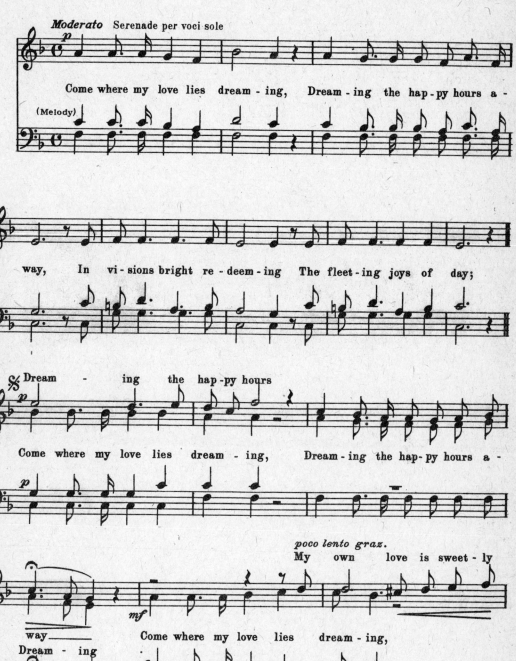

SUMMER LONGINGS

Published by W. C. Peters, Baltimore, 1849.

The author of the verses is Denis Florence MacCarthy, an Irish poet (1817-1882). Stephen evidently found the words in the *Home Journal*, and set them to music of his own composition.

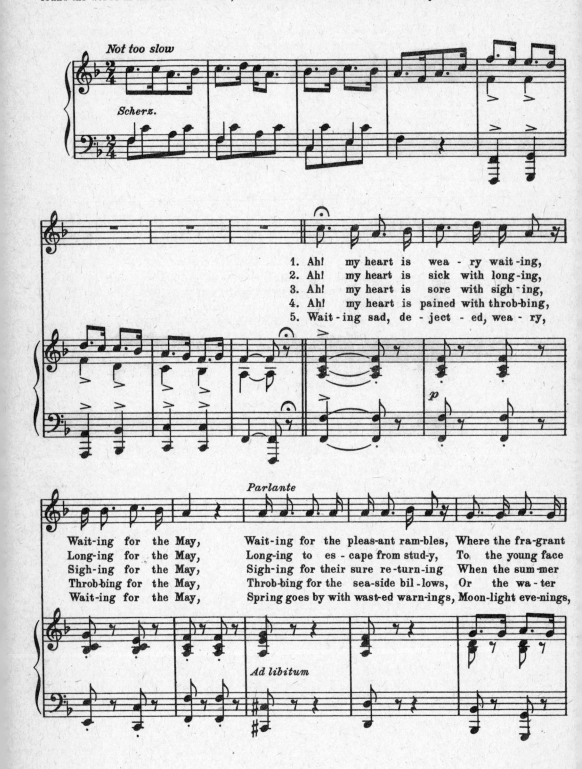

a tempo

haw - thorn bram-bles, With the wood-bine al - ter-na - ting, Scent the dew - y
fair and rud - dy, And the thou-sand charms be-long-ing To the sum-mer's
beams are burn-ing, Hopes and flow'rs that dead or dy - ing All the win - ter
woo - ing wil - lows; Where in laugh-ing and in sob-bing Glide the streams a -
sun - bright morn-ings; Sum - mer comes, yet dark and drear-y Life still ebbs a -

way. Ah! my heart is wear - y wait-ing,
day. Ah! my heart is sick with long-ing,
lay. Ah! my heart is sore with sigh-ing,
way. Ah! my heart, my heart is throb-bing,
way. Man is ev - er wea - ry, wea - ry,

Wait - ing for the May.
Long - ing for the May.
Sigh - ing for the May.
Throb - bing for the May.
Wait - ing for the May.

JEANIE WITH THE LIGHT BROWN HAIR

Published by Firth, Pond & Co.,1854.

Stephen's wife was Jane McDowell Foster. He called her Jennie or Jeanie. He evidently had her in mind when he wrote this song.

Moderato

1. I dream of Jea - nie with the light brown hair,
2. I long for Jea - nie with the day dawn smile,
3. I sigh for Jea - nie, but her light form strayed

Borne, like a va - por, on the sum-mer air; I see her trip-ping where the
Ra - diant in glad -ness, warm with win-ning guile; I hear her mel - o - dies, like
Far from the fond hearts 'round her na -tive glade; Her smiles have van-ished and her

bright streams play, Hap - py as the dai - sies that dance on her way.
joys gone by, Sigh-ing 'round my heart o'er the fond hopes that die:
sweet songs flown, Flit-ting like the dreams that have cheered us and gone.

Ma - ny were the wild notes her mer-ry voice would pour, Ma - ny were the blithe birds that
Sigh-ing like the night wind and sob-bing like the rain, Wail-ing for the lost one that
Now the nod-ding wild flow'rs may with-er on the shore While her gen-tle fin - gers will

ad lib.

war - bled them o'er: Oh!___ I dream of Jea - nie with the light brown hair,
comes not a - gain: Oh!___ I long for Jea - nie and my heart bows low,
cull them no more: Oh!___ I sigh for Jea - nie with the light brown hair,

Float - ing, like a va - por, on the soft sum - mer air.
Nev - er - more to find her where the bright wa - ters flow.
Float - ing, like a va - por, on the soft sum - mer air.

rall

8va - - - - - - - - - - - - - - - - *loco*

ANGELINA BAKER

Published by F. D. Benteen, Baltimore, 1850.

This is an excellent example of one of Foster's songs "in lighter vein"

This chorus includes the phrase, "beat on de old jaw bone." A jaw bone was a musical instrument used in the early minstrel shows, before their music was of as high a quality as in later years. The jaw bone consisted of half of a horse's jaw bone, which was dried until it would give a hollow sound when struck. The teeth were kept in the jaw, and being loose their rattling added to the noise. There seem to have been generally two jaw bones in a band. Beating time with them must have added a considerable amount of merriment to the show.

1. __ 'Way down on de old plan - ta - tion Dah's where I was born, I used to beat de whole cre - a - tion Hoe - in' in de corn: Oh! den I work and den I sing So hap - py all de day, 'Till

2. I've seen my An - ge - li - na In de spring-time and de fall, I've seen her in de corn-field And I've seen her at de ball; And eb - ry time I met her She was smil - ing like de sun, But

3. __ An - ge - li - na am so tall She neb - ber sees de ground, She hab to take a wel - lum-scope To look down on de town. __ An - ge - li - na likes de boys As far as she can see dem, She

4. __ Ear - ly in de morn-ing Ob a lob - ly sum - mer day I ax for An - ge - li - na, And dey say, "she's gone a - way." I don't know wha to find her, Cayse I don't know wha she's gone, She

An - ge - li - na Ba - ker came And stole my heart a - way.
now I'm left to weep a tear Cayse An - ge - li - na's gone.
used to run old Mas - sa round To ax him for to free dem.
left me here to weep a tear And beat on de old jaw - bone.

CHORUS

An - ge - li - na Bak - er! An - ge - li - na Bak - er's gone, She

left me here to weep a tear And beat on de old jaw - bone.

OLD UNCLE NED

The first edition was issued by William E. Millet of New York. It was copyrighted May 16, 1848.

The Millet edition was pirated. Since it contains differences in both the words and music from the version authorized by Foster himself, it cannot be accepted as the standard.

The edition considered the standard was authorized by Foster. It was published by W. C. Peters & Co. of Louisville and was copyrighted December 30, 1848.

Morrison Foster says of this song: "In 1845 a club of young men, friends of his, met twice a week at our house to practice songs in harmony under his leadership. At that time negro melodies were very popular. After we had sung over and over again all the songs then in favor, he proposed that he would try and make some for us himself. His first effort was called *The Louisiana Belle*. A week after this he produced the famous song of *Old Uncle Ned*. *Old Uncle Ned* immediately became known and popular everywhere. Both the words and melody are remarkable. At the time he wrote 'His Fingers Were Long Like de Cane in de Brake,' he had never seen a canebrake, nor even been below the mouth of the Ohio River, but the appropriateness of the simile instantly strikes everyone who has traveled down the Mississippi."

Harold Vincent Milligan says: "*Old Uncle Ned* became enormously popular at once, and has always been one of the best-known of Foster's melodies. It is the first of the pathetic negro songs that set Foster apart from his contemporaries and gave him a place in musical history. In this type of song, universal in the appeal of its naive pathos, he has never had an equal."

1. Dere was an old dark-ey, dey called him Un-cle Ned, He's dead long a-go, long a-go! He had no wool on de top ob his head, De

gone whar de good dark-eys go.

gone whar de good dark-eys go.

2. His fin-gers were long like de cane in de brake, He had no eyes for to
3. When Old Ned die Mas-sa take it might-y bad, De tears run down like de

see; He had no teeth for to eat de corn cake So he
rain; Old Mis-sus turn pale, and she gets ber-ry sad Cayse she

Bass Voice

had to let de corn cake be. Den lay down de shub-ble and de hoe____
neb-ber see Old Ned a-gain. Den lay down de shub-ble and de hoe____

[27]

Hang up de fid-dle and de bow: No more hard work for

Hang up de fid-dle and de bow: No more hard work for

poor Old Ned He's gone whar de good dark-eys go.

poor Old Ned He's gone whar de good dark-eys go.

No more hard work for poor Old Ned He's gone whar de good dark-eys go.

No more hard work for poor Old Ned He's gone whar de good dark-eys go.

THE MERRY, MERRY MONTH OF MAY

SONG AND QUARTETTE

1. We roamed the fields and riv - er sides, When we were young and gay; We
2. Our voic - es ech - oed through the glen With blithe and joy - ful ring; We
3. We joyed to meet and griev'd to part, We sigh'd when night came on; We

chased the bees and pluck'd the flow'rs, In the mer - ry, mer-ry month of May. Oh,
built our huts of mos - sy stones, And we dab-bled in the hill - side spring. Oh,
went to rest with long - ing heart, For the com-ing of the bright-day dawn. Oh,

yes, with ev - er chang - ing sports, We whiled the hours a - way; The

skies were bright, Our hearts were light, In the mer-ry, mer-ry month of May.

QUARTETTE

Moderato

1. We roamed the fields and riv-er sides When we were young and gay; We
2. Our voic-es ech-oed through the glen With blithe and joy-ful ring; We
3. We joyed to meet and grieved to part, We sigh'd when night came on; We

chased the bees and plucked the flow'rs, In the mer-ry, mer-ry month of May. Oh,
built our huts of mos-sy stones, And we dab-bled in the hill-side spring. Oh,
went to rest with long-ing heart, For the com-ing of the bright-day dawn. Oh,

yes, with ev-er chang-ing sports, We whiled the hours a-way; The

skies were bright, Our hearts were light, In the mer-ry, mer-ry month of May.

MY BRUDDER GUM

Published by Firth, Pond & Co.,1849.

This was one of Stephen's two first songs to be published by Firth, Pond & Co.(The other was *Nelly was a Lady*) Stephen received no royalties for these two songs. Apparently his only pay for them was fifty copies of each.

After these two songs were published, Stephen entered into a contract with Firth, Pond & Co., the terms of which gave him 2¢ a copy for his future publications, after the expenses of publication were paid. Later contracts increased his royalties with more favorable terms.

[31]

All de yal - ler gals run - nin' round, Try to get a lock ob his hair.

2d V. Hard work all de day, Hab no time to play,

Ber - ry fine time a - dig - gin' in de corn - field, Hay! Brud - der Gum. *Chorus*

3d V. Tud - der af - ter - noon, I thought I saw de moon,

Saw my true lub com - in' through de cane - brake, Hay! Brud - der Gum. *Chorus*

4th V. Went one ber - ry fine day, To ride in a one - horse sleigh,

Hol - low'd to de old hoss com - in' through de toll gate, Hay! Brud - der Gum. *Chorus*

NELL AND I

Moderato

1. We part - ed in the spring - time of life, Nell and I, With
2. We made our lit - tle huts on the shore, Nell and I, And
3. We wan - dered by the bright run - ning streams, Nell and I, And

all our gush-ing joys in their bloom, But now we've met the world's bus - y
cov - ered them with bright col-ored shells, We gath-ered moss and fern from the
gam-boled o'er the wide gras - sy lawn, We met a - gain in light, sport-ive

strife, Nell and I, And suf - fered from its dark chill - ing gloom.
moor, Nell and I, And pluck'd the dew - y flow'rs from the dells.
dreams, Nell and I, When the wea - ry hours of twi - light had flown.

Yet my heart will sigh For those days gone by, That
But the days roll'd round And the rude world frown'd As
And our hearts proved true 'Till a cold-ness grew, 'Twas

flow in my mem-'ry's sweet re-frain. We part-ed in the spring-time of
time with its bit-ter cares fled on. We left our lit-tle huts on the
caused by some un-re-lent-ing foe. We'll roam up-on the lawn nev-er-

life, Nell and I, And I'll nev-er see her bright smiles a-gain.
shore, Nell and I, And we left our bright-est hopes in their dawn.
more, Nell and I, Nor__ wan-der where the bright riv-ers flow.

RING, RING DE BANJO!

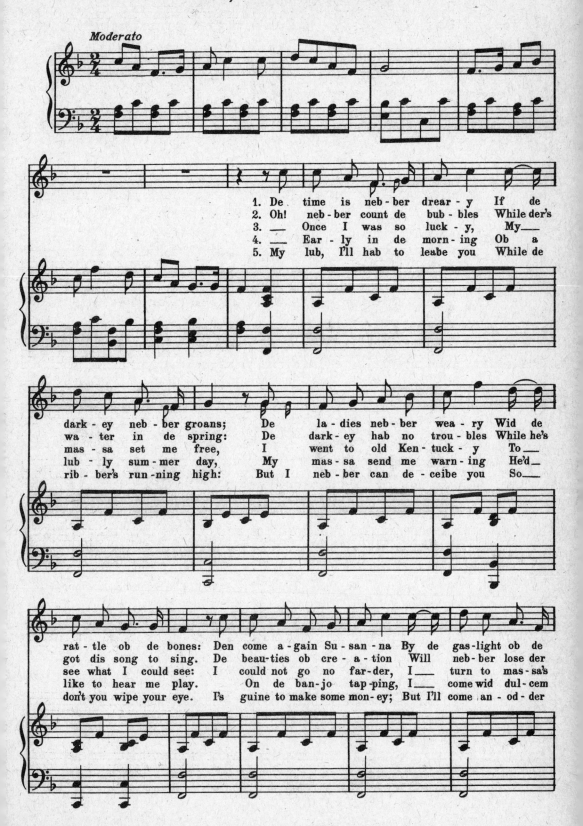

Moderato

1. De time is neb-ber drear-y If de
2. Oh! neb-ber count de bub-bles While der's
3. — Once I was so luck-y, My—
4. — Ear-ly in de morn-ing Ob a
5. My lub, I'll hab to leabe you While de

dark-ey neb-ber groans; De la-dies neb-ber wea-ry Wid de
wa-ter in de spring: De dark-ey hab no trou-bles While he's
mas-sa set me free, I went to old Ken-tuck-y To—
lub-ly sum-mer day, My mas-sa send me warn-ing He'd—
rib-ber's run-ning high: But I neb-ber can de-ceibe you So—

rat-tle ob de bones: Den come a-gain Su-san-na By de gas-light ob de
got dis song to sing. De beau-ties ob cre-a-tion Will neb-ber lose der
see what I could see: I could not go no far-der, I— turn to mas-sa's
like to hear me play. On de ban-jo tap-ping, I— come wid dul-cem
don't you wipe your eye. I's guine to make some mon-ey; But I'll come an-od-der

[35]

moon; We'll tum de old Pi - a - no When de ban-jo's out ob tune.
charm While I roam de old plan - ta - tion Wid my true lub on my arm.
door, I lub him all de har-der, I'll__ go a - way no more.
strain; I'll Mas - sa fall a - nap-ping, He'll__ neb-ber wake a - gain.
day; I'll come a - gain my hon - ey, If I hab to work my way.

CHORUS

Ring, ring de ban - jo! I like dat good old song,

true lub! Oh,

Come a - gain my own true lub! Oh, wha you been so long.

true lub! Oh,

THE HOUR FOR THEE AND ME
DUET

1. When day breaks forth on the dew-y lawn, And all seems mirth and glee, When

birds their sweet-est songs a-wake Is the hour for thee and me___ The

hour for thee and me, The hour for thee and me, When

birds their sweet-est songs a-wake Is the hour for thee and me.

2. When per-fumes from the clos-ing flow'rs Are waft-ed o'er the lea, And
3. When night be - holds her star - ry realm Re-flect-ed on the sea, When

ves - pers float up - on the gale, Is the hour for thee and me, The
moon-beams dance up - on the rill, Is the hour for thee and me, The

hour for thee and me, The hour for thee and me, When
hour for thee and me, The hour for thee and me, When

ves - pers float up - on the gale Is the hour for thee and me.
moon-beams dance up - on the rill Is the hour for thee and me.

HARD TIMES, COME AGAIN NO MORE

Published by Firth, Pond & Co., the song was copyrighted January 17, 1855, but the title page bears the date 1854. It was probably published late in 1854 and then copyrighted in January 1855.

Morrison Foster tells the story of Olivia Pise, a maid in the Foster household, who was a member of a church for colored people. He writes: "She was permitted to often take Stephen to church with her. Here he stored up in his mind 'many a gem of purest ray serene', drawn from these caves of negro melody. The number of strains heard there, and which, he said to me, were too good to be lost, have been preserved by him, short scraps of which were incorporated in two of his songs, *Hard Times Come Again No More* and *Oh! Boys, Carry Me Long*.

1. Let us pause in life's pleas-ures and count its man-y tears While we
2. While we seek mirth and beau-ty and mu-sic light and gay There are
3. There's a pale droop-ing maid-en who toils her life a-way With a
4. 'Tis a sigh that is waft-ed a-cross the trou-bled wave, 'Tis a

all sup sor-row with the poor: There's a song that will lin-ger for-
frail forms faint-ing at the door: Though their voic-es are si-lent, their
worn heart whose bet-ter days are o'er: Though her voice would be mer-ry, 'tis
wail that is heard up-on the shore, 'Tis a dirge that is mur-mured a-

ev - er in our ears; Oh! Hard Times, come a - gain no more.
plead-ing looks will say, Oh! Hard Times, come a - gain no more.
sigh - ing all the day, Oh! Hard Times, come a - gain no more.
round the low - ly grave, Oh! Hard Times, come a - gain no more.

CHORUS

'Tis the song, the sigh of the wea - ry; Hard Times, Hard Times, come a-gain no more: Man-y

days you have lin-gered a - round my cab-in door; Oh! Hard Times, come a-gain no more.

Way down upon de old plantation

Way down upon de Pedee ribber
Far far away

Dere's where my heart is turning ebber
Deres wha my brudders play

Way down upon de Savanee ribber
Far far away

Dere's where my heart is turning ebber
Dere's where de old folks stay

All up and down de whole creation
Sadly I roam

Still longing for de old plantation
And for de old folks at home

OLD FOLKS AT HOME
Original Manuscript

OLD FOLKS AT HOME

Published by Firth, Pond & Co., 1851.

Harold Vincent Milligan says: "*Old Folks at Home* is Foster's chief claim to remembrance. Aside from one or two national airs, born of great historical crises, such as the *Marseillaise*, this is probably the most widely known and loved song ever written. It has been translated into every European language and into many Asian and African tongues. It has been sung by millions the world over and has long since passed out of the realm of written song to be incorporated into the body of folk-music passed orally from generation to generation, breathing the very soul of the people."

Brother Morrison tells the story of the song's composition as follows:

"One day in 1851, Stephen came into my office, on the bank of the Monongahela, Pittsburgh, and said to me, 'What is a good name of two syllables for a Southern river? I want to use it in this new song of *Old Folks at Home*.' I asked him how Yazoo would do. 'Oh,' said he, 'that has been used before.' I then suggested Pedee. 'Oh,' pshaw, he replied, I won't have that.' I then took down an atlas from the top of my desk and opened the map of the United States. We both looked over it and my finger stopped at the 'Swanee', a little river in Florida emptying into the Gulf of Mexico. 'That's it, that's it exactly', exclaimed he delighted, as he wrote the name down; and the song was finished, commencing, 'Way Down Upon de Swanee Ribber.' He left the office, as was his custom, abruptly, without saying another word, and I resumed my work."

Foster's original manuscript of *Old Folks at Home* shows that his first title was "Way down upon de old plantation." The first verse was:

> "Way down upon de Pedee ribber
> Far, far away
> Dere's where my heart is turning ebber
> Dere's wha my brudders play."

The second attempt shows "Pedee" crossed out, and "Swanee" written just above it:

> Swanee
> "Way down upon de ~~Pedee~~ ribber
> Far far away
> Dere's where my heart is turning ebber
> Dere's where de old folks stay."

1. 'Way down up-on de Swa-nee rib-ber, Far, far a-way, Dere's wha my heart is turn-ing eb-ber, Dere's wha de old folks stay.

All up and down de whole cre-a-tion, Sad-ly I roam,

Still long-ing for de old plan-ta-tion, And for de old folks at home.

CHORUS

All de world am sad and drear-y, Eb-ry-where I roam,

Oh! dark-eys how my heart grows wea-ry, Far from de old folks at home.

All round de lit-tle farm I wan-dered When I was young, Den man-y hap-py

days I squan-dered, Man-y de songs I sung. When I was play-ing wid my brud-der

Hap-py was I, Oh! take me to my kind old mud-der, Dere let me live and die. (Cho.)

One lit-tle hut a-mong de bush-es, One dat I love, Still sad-ly to my

mem-'ry rush-es, No mat-ter where I rove, When will I see de bees a-hum-ming

All round de comb? When will I hear de ban-jo tum-ming Down in my good old home? (Cho.)

OPEN THY LATTICE, LOVE

Published by George Willig, Philadelphia, 1844.

Morrison Foster says: "At sixteen years of age he produced his first published song. It was called *Open Thy Lattice, Love*. The music only was his."

Stephen found the verses to *Open Thy Lattice, Love* in *The New Mirror* a Saturday paper edited in New York by George P. Morris and Nathaniel P. Willis. The verses were written by George P. Morris, and they appeared in the *Mirror* in the autumn of 1843, so that Stephen would seem to have been 17, rather than 16, when the music was composed.

John Tasker Howard says: "The poem had been set to music by another composer several years earlier, a fact noted under the title of the poem when printed in the *New Mirror*. Joseph Philip Knight, the English song-writer who composed the music to Emma Willard's poem, *Rocked in the Cradle of the Deep* while he was in America in 1839, made a setting of *Open Thy Lattice, Love*, published in 1840. It is interesting to compare Knight's music with the song Stephen composed. Knight's setting is more musicianly, more resourceful in the development of its melodic idea. Stephen's song is far more spontaneous and is often sung today, while Knight's is forgotten."

1. O- pen thy lat-tice, love, lis-ten to me!   The cool balm-y breeze is a-broad on the sea!   The moon like a queen, roams her realms of blue, And the
2. O- pen thy lat-tice, love, lis-ten to me!   In the voy-age of life Love our pi-lot will be!   He will sit at the helm__ wher-ev-er we rove,__ And

stars keep their vi-gils in heav-en for you. Ere morn's gush-ing light tips the
steer by the lode-star he kin-dled a-bove. His shell for a shal-lop will

hills with its ray, A - way o'er the wa-ters, a - way and a - way! Then
cut the bright spray, Or skim like a bird o'er the wa - ters a - way; Then

o - pen thy lat-tice, love, lis - ten to me! While the moon's in the sky and the
o - pen thy lat-tice, love, lis - ten to me! While the moon's in the sky and the

breeze on the sea!
breeze on the sea!

pp

NELLY BLY

Published by Firth, Pond & Co., 1850.

Harold Vincent Milligan says: *"Nelly Bly* is so typically a folk-song that it seems difficult to believe that it was ever 'written' by anybody. It is one of those simple little tunes that seem to go on their carefree way as inevitably as sunlight or the laughter of little children. It is one of the few happy songs ever written by Stephen Foster. Aside from the jingling nonsense of the minstrel songs, he turned instinctively to sentimental melancholy, the yearnings of homesickness and sad memories of the past. *Nelly Bly* is a song of contentment and plenty, more truly characteristic of the negro than *My Brudder Gum* or *Oh! Susanna."*

1. Nel-ly Bly! Nel-ly Bly! Bring de broom a-long, We'll sweep de kitch-en clean, my dear, and hab a lit-tle song. Poke de wood, my la-dy lub, And make de fire burn, And while I take de ban-jo down, Just gib de mush a turn.

Heigh! Nel-ly, Ho! Nel-ly, lis-ten, lub, to me, I'll sing for you, play for you, a

dul-cem mel-o-dy. Heigh! Nel-ly, Ho! Nel-ly, lis-ten, lub, to me, I'll

sing for you, play for you, a dul-cem mel-o-dy.

2d V. Nel - ly Bly hab a voice like de tur - tle dove, I hears it in de mead-ow and I hears it in de grove. Nel - ly Bly hab a heart warm as cup ob tea, And big-ger dan de sweet po - ta - to down in Ten-nes - see.

Chorus

3d V. Nel - ly Bly shuts her eye when she goes to sleep, When she wak-ens up a - gain her eye-balls gin to peep. De way she walks she lifts her foot, and den she brings it down, And when it lights der's mu - sic dah in dat part ob de town.

Chorus

4th V. Nel - ly Bly! Nel - ly Bly! Neb - ber, neb - ber sigh, Neb-ber bring de tear-drop to de cor - ner ob your eye, For de pie is made ob pun-kins and de mush is made ob corn, And der's corn and pun-kins plen - ty, lub, a - ly - in' in de barn.

Chorus

OUR BRIGHT SUMMER DAYS ARE GONE

Published by John J. Daly, New York, 1861.

John Mahon, a friend of Stephen Foster during his last years in New York, tells the story of the writing of this song:

"Foster wrote and composed most of his latest songs in my rooms, in Henry Street. One of these, and a most beautiful one, *Our Bright Summer Days Are Gone*, he took to Firth, Pond & Co., who refused it for some reason or other, and it made him feel very despondent. I remember one evening, when we were both pretty hard up—indeed, neither of us had a cent, and I had a family besides—suddenly he sat down to the piano."

" 'John', said he, 'I haven't time to write a new song, but I think I can write *Our Bright Summer Days Are Gone* from memory.' "

"He sat down, and wrote the words and music from memory in about an hour and a half."

" 'Take this 'round to Daly,' said he, 'and take what he will give you.' "

"Mr. John J. Daly was then my publisher. I took the song to Mr. Daly. He was proud to get a song from Foster. He tried it over, and it was really beautiful. He offered a sum which, though not a tithe of what Foster got in his better days, was still considered very handsome. This song became very popular."

Moderato, con espressione

1. I re-mem-ber the days of our youth and love, When we sat 'neath the green oak tree; When thy
2. I re-mem-ber the flow'rs that we cull'd by day, And the vows that we made by night; I re-
3. How we joyed when we met, and grievd to part, How we sighed when the night came on; How I

smiles were bright as the skies a-bove, And thy voice made mu-sic un-to me.
mem-ber the brook where we loved to stray In the by-gone days of our de-light.
longed for thee in my dream-ing heart, Till the first fair com-ing of the dawn.

CHORUS

Nev-er more will come those hap-py, hap-py hours, Whiled a-way in life's young dawn;

Nev-er more we'll roam thro' pleasure's sunny bow'rs, For our bright, bright summer days are gone.

COME WITH THY SWEET VOICE AGAIN

1. Come with thy sweet voice a-gain, To my heart still dear,
2. Bring not a lan-guage that tells How the light hours roll:

La - den with soft sooth-ing pain, Like a tear, like a tear.
Come with the mu-sic that wells From thy soul, from thy soul.

Bright vi-sions, long van-ished Round thy mel-o-dies beam:___
Come not with bright off-'rings, Cold, un-hal-lowed and new:___

Lulled in the lap of thy sighs, Let me dream, let me dream. Come a-
Bring but thine own gen-tle heart, Ev-er true,___ ev-er true.

gain ___ Come with thy sweet voice a - gain ___

Come, oh! Come a - gain, ___ Come with thy sweet voice a - gain. ___

mf *p*

mf *p*

[54]

OH! BOYS, CARRY ME 'LONG

Published by Firth, Pond & Co., 1851.

Morrison Foster's comment on *Hard Times Come Again No More* (page 40) applies to this song also.

1. Oh! car-ry me 'long; Der's no more trou-ble for me: I's guine to roam In a hap-py home Where all de dark-eys am free. I've worked long in de fields; I've han-dled ma-ny a

2. All o-ber de land I've wan-dered ma-ny a day, To blow de horn And mind de corn And keep de pos-sum a-way. No use for me now So dark-eys, bur-y me

3. Fare-well to de boys Wid hearts so hap-py and light, Dey sing a song De whole day long, And dance de ju-ba at night. Fare-well to de fields Ob cot-ton, 'bac-co, and

4. Fare-well to de hills, De mead-ows cov-ered wid green, Old brin-dle Boss And de old grey hoss All beat-en, brok-en, and lean. Fare-well to de dog Dat al-ways fol-lowed me

hoe: ___ I'll turn my eye, Be - fore I die, And see de su-gar cane grow.___
low: ___ My horn is dry, And I must lie Wha de pos-sum neb-ber can go. ___
all: ___ I's guine to hoe In a bress-ed row Wha de corn grows mel-low and tall.___
round; ___ Old San-cho'll wail And droop his tail When I am un-der de ground.

CHORUS

Oh! boys car - ry me 'long; Car - ry me till I die ___

Car - ry me down to de bur - y - in' groun'. Mas - sa, don't you cry.___

HAPPY HOURS AT HOME

Moderato

1. I sit me down by my own fire-side When the win-ter nights come on, And I calm-ly dream, as the dim hours glide, Of man-y pleas-ant scenes now gone; Of our health-ful plays in my schoolboy days, That can nev-er come a-gain; Of our

2. I sit me down by my own fire-side Where the chil-dren sport in glee, While the clear young voice of our household pride Makes mel-o-dy that's dear to me. And by ev-'ry art that can charm the heart, They al-lure my cares a-way, To pre-

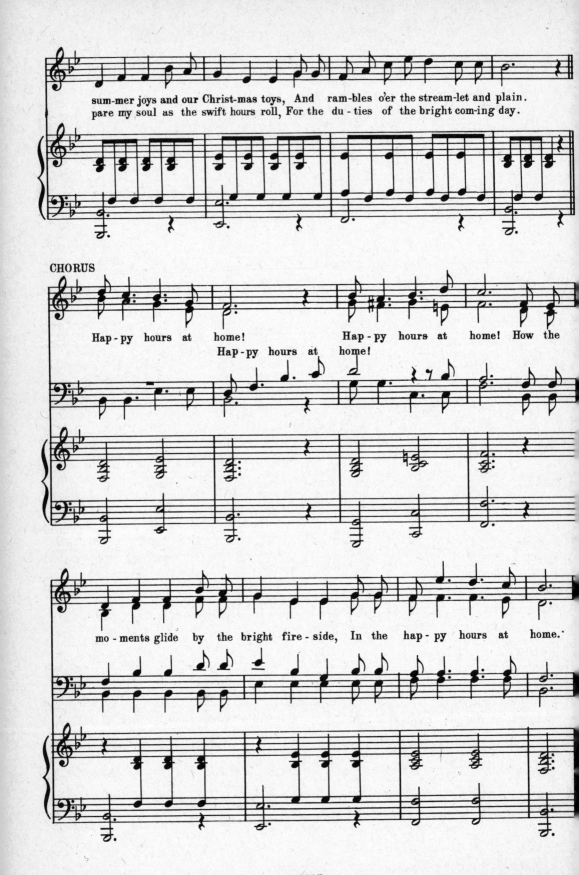

sum-mer joys and our Christ-mas toys, And ram-bles o'er the stream-let and plain.
pare my soul as the swift hours roll, For the du - ties of the bright com-ing day.

CHORUS

Hap - py hours at home! Hap - py hours at home! How the
Hap - py hours at home!

mo - ments glide by the bright fire - side, In the hap - py hours at home.

DOWN AMONG THE CANE BRAKES

Published by Firth, Pond & Co., 1860.

1. Once I could laugh and play, When in life's ear-ly day;
2. Yes I was free from care; All was bright sum-mer there;
3. There lived my moth-er dear (Gone from this world I fear);
4. There lived a love-ly one, Who, like the rest, has gone;
5. Long years have glid-ed by Since then I breathed each sigh;

Then I was far a-way, Down a-mong the cane-brakes.
Dark days to me were fair, Down a-mong the cane-brakes.
There rang our voic-es clear, Down a-mong the cane-brakes.
She might have been my own, Down a-mong the cane-brakes.
May I re-turn to die, Down a-mong the cane-brakes.

Down a - mong the cane-brakes on the Mis - sis - sip - pi shore,

Oh! Those hap-py days, those hap-py days are o'er! Oh! Those hap-py days will

come back no more!

a tempo

OLD BLACK JOE

Published by Firth, Pond & Co., 1860.

Old Black Joe is one of the last songs which Foster wrote before he left Pittsburgh in 1860 and went to New York, where he remained until his death. It is one of the most sincere of all Foster's works. We can see that the emotions expressed in its verses are genuine when we think about his domestic affairs. Stephen was a person who loved his old home and family—these were almost gone. His beloved mother and father were dead. His two sisters were married and had left Pittsburgh. Two brothers had died. Another brother, Morrison, who was closest to him in age and affection, had married and gone to live in Cleveland, leaving Stephen practically alone in Pittsburgh, except for his wife and daughter.

1. Gone are the days when my heart was young and gay,
2. Why do I weep when my heart should feel no pain,
3. Where are the hearts once so hap-py and so free? The

Gone are my friends from the cot-ton fields a-way, Gone from the earth to a
Why do I sigh that my friends come not a-gain, Griev-ing for forms now de-
chil-dren so dear that I held up-on my knee, Gone to the shore where my

bet - ter land I know, I hear their gen-tle voic-es call-ing "Old Black Joe."
part-ed long a-go? I hear their gen-tle voic-es call-ing "Old Black Joe."
soul has longed to go. I hear their gen-tle voic-es call-ing "Old Black Joe."

CHORUS

I'm com-ing, I'm com-ing, for my head is bend-ing low: I hear those gen-tle voic-es call-ing

I'm com-ing, I'm com-ing, for my head is bend-ing low: I hear those gen-tle voic-es call-ing

"Old Black Joe."

"Old Black Joe."

BEAUTIFUL CHILD OF SONG

Poco lento

1. Come, I am long-ing to hear thee, Beau-ti-ful child of song,—
2. Come, for the spell of a fai - ry Dwells in thy mag-ic-al voice,—

Come though the hearts that are near thee, A - round thee de - vot - ed - ly throng.
And at thy step, light and air - y, E'en cold hearts en - rap-tured re - joice.—

Come, I am long-ing to hear thee, Beau-ti-ful child of song,
Beau-ti-ful child of song, I'm
long-ing to hear thee car-ol thy lay, sweet child of song.

GENTLE ANNIE

Andante mosso

1. Thou wilt come no more, gen-tle An-nie, Like a

flow'r thy spir-it did de-part; Thou art gone, a-las! like the

man-y That have bloomed in the sum-mer of my heart.

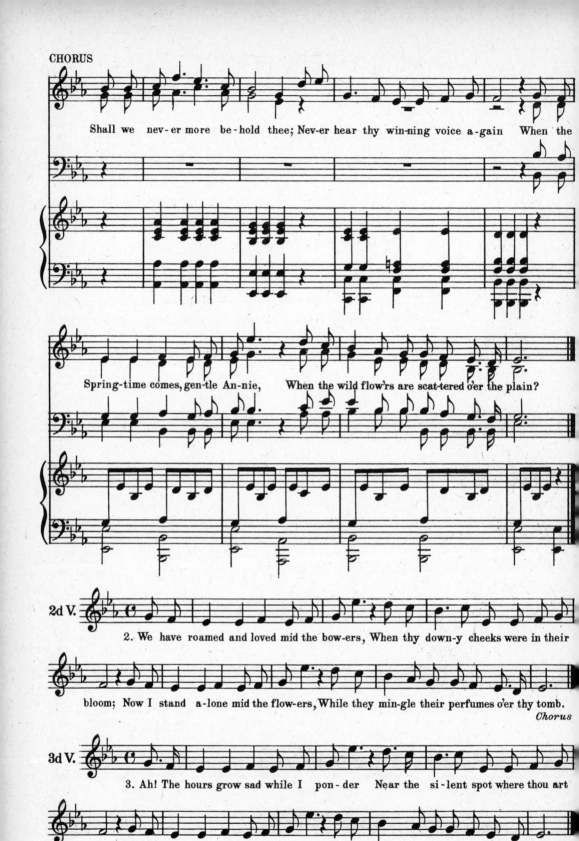

Shall we nev-er more be-hold thee; Nev-er hear thy win-ning voice a-gain When the

Spring-time comes, gen-tle An-nie, When the wild flow'rs are scat-tered o'er the plain?

2d V.

2. We have roamed and loved mid the bow-ers, When thy down-y cheeks were in their

bloom; Now I stand a-lone mid the flow-ers, While they min-gle their perfumes o'er thy tomb.
Chorus

3d V.

3. Ah! The hours grow sad while I pon-der Near the si-lent spot where thou art

laid, And my heart bows down when I wan-der By the streams and the meadows where we stray'd.
Chorus

FAREWELL MY LILLY DEAR

Moderato

1. Oh! Lil - ly dear, it grieves me The
2. I's guine to roam the wide world In
3. I wake up in the morn - ing And
4. Oh! Lil - ly dear, 'tis mourn - ful To

tale I have to tell; Old mas - sa sends me roam - ing, So Lil - ly, fare - you-
lands I've nev - er hoed, With noth-ing but my ban - jo To cheer me on the
walk out on the farm; Oh! Lil - ly am a dar - ling, She take me by the
leave you here a - lone; You'll smile be -fore I leave you And weep when I am

well! Oh! fare - you-well, my true love, Fare - well old Ten - nes - see. Then
road; For when I'm sad and wea - ry I'll make the ban - jo play, To
arm; We wan - der through the clov - er Down by the riv - er side; I
gone. The sun can nev - er shine, love, So bright for you and me, As

let me weep for you, love, But do not weep for me.
mind me of my true love When I am far a - way.
tell her that I love her And she must be my bride.
when I worked be - side you In good old Ten - nes - see.

CHORUS

Fare - well for - ev - er to old Ten - nes - see; Fare - well, my

Lil - ly dear, Don't weep for me.

Repeat Cho.

[68]

FAIRY BELLE

Published by Firth, Pond & Co., 1859.

Stephen was probably describing this song when he wrote to his brother, Morrison, on June 13, 1859. "I sent off a first-rate song the other day to Firth, Pond & Co. When I receive a printed copy I will send it to you."

1. The pride of the vil - lage and the fair - est in the dell Is the queen of my song, and her name is Fair-y Belle; The sound of her light step may be heard up - on the hill Like the fall of the snow-drop or the drip-ping of the rill.

2d V. She sings to the mead-ows and she car-ols to the streams, She laughs in the sun-light and smiles while in her dreams, Her hair like the this-tle down is borne up-on the air, And her heart, like the hum-ming bird's, is free from ev-'ry care. *Chorus*

3d V. Her soft notes of mel-o-dy a-round me sweet-ly fall, Her eye full of love is now beam-ing on my soul. The sound of that gen-tle voice, the glance of that eye, Sur-round me with rap-ture that no oth-er heart could sigh. *Chorus*

MASSA'S IN DE COLD GROUND

Published by Firth. Pond & Co., 1852.

Tradition states that Stephen was inspired to write this song by the grief felt at the death of his beloved father; but the song was published in 1852 and William Foster, his father, died in 1855. Whether any specific experience prompted the song is a matter of doubt; but its deep sincerity and pathos are none the less appealing, whatever its origin.

1. Round de mead-ows am a - ring - ing De dark-eys' mourn-ful song,

While de mock-ing bird am sing - ing, Hap-py as de day am long.

Where de i-vy am a-creep-ing O'er de grass-y mound,

Dare old mas-sa am a-sleep-ing, Sleep-ing in de cold, cold ground.

CHORUS

1st Voice

Down in de corn-field Hear dat mourn-ful sound:

2d Voice

All de dark-eys am a-weep-ing, Mas-sa's in de cold, cold ground.

Repeat Cho.

[73]

2d V. When de au-tumn leaves were fall-ing, When de days were cold, 'Twas hard to hear old mas-sa call-ing, Cayse he was so weak and old.

Now de o-range tree am bloom-ing On de san-dy shore,

Now de sum-mer days am com-ing, Mas-sa neb-ber calls no more. *Chorus*

3d V. Mas-sa made de dark-eys love him, Cayse he was so kind,

Now dey sad-ly weep a-bove him, Mourn-ing cayse he leave dem be-hind. I

can-not work be-fore to-mor-row, Cayse de tear drop flow. I

try to drive a-way my sor-row Pick-in' on de old ban-jo. *Chorus*

OLD DOG TRAY

Published by Firth, Pond & Co., 1853.

Morrison Foster has the following to say about *Old Dog Tray*. "An old friend of ours, Col. Matthew I. Stewart, gave Stephen a handsome setter dog, which for a long time was his constant companion. We lived upon the East Common of Allegheny, a wide open space. Stephen often watched this dog with much plea - sure, playing with the children on the Common. When he wrote of *Old Dog Tray*, he put into verse and song the sentiments elicited by remembrances of this faithful dog."

1. The morn of life is past, And eve-ning comes at last; It brings me a dream of a once hap-py day, Of mer-ry forms I've seen Up-on the vil-lage green, Sport-ing with my old dog Tray.

OLD DOG TRAY

Old dog Tray's ev-er faith - ful, Grief can-not drive him a-

way. He's gen-tle, he is kind; I'll nev-er, nev-er find A

bet-ter friend than old dog Tray.

2. The forms I call'd my own Have
3. When thoughts re-call the past His

van-ished one by one, The lov'd ones, the dear ones have all passed a - way. Their
eyes are on me cast; I know that he feels what my break-ing heart would say: Al -

hap-py smiles have flown, Their gen-tle voic-es gone; I've noth-ing left but old dog Tray.
though he can-not speak I'll vain- ly, vain-ly seek A bet-ter friend than old dog Tray.

CHORUS

Old dog Tray's ev - er faith - ful, Grief can-not drive him a - way, He's

gen-tle, he is kind; I'll nev-er, nev-er find A bet-ter friend than old dog Tray.

OH! SUSANNA

The edition of this song which was authorized by Stephen Foster himself, and which probably prints the music as Foster wrote it, was published in Louisville by W. C. Peters & Co., in 1848. This edition was copyrighted December 30, 1848. Just above the music on page three appears "Susanna, as sung by Mr. Tichnor of the Sable Harmonists. Written and composed by S. C. Foster."

However, many music publishers issued "pirated" editions of *Oh! Susanna* before Peters got his authorized version on the market. Most of these show errors in both the words and music, and can not be considered the song as Stephen wrote it. The earliest of these pirated editions so far discovered was published by C. Holt, Jr., in New York in 1848. It was copyrighted February 25, 1848.

Nothing is known about the writing of this song. It has been said that it was composed in Pittsburgh for a group of musical friends (see note to *Old Uncle Ned*) but this statement cannot be verified. Nor can it be proved that Cincinnati was the city of composition, although it seems somewhat more likely. This is a controversy which may never be satisfactorily settled.

Wherever the song was composed, it became immediately popular. It was sung, not only in the United States, but all the world over. Travellers of the time reported having heard it in many countries. The Forty-niners on their way to the gold fields of California adopted the song as their national anthem. Foster's words were often changed to fit local persons, localities, or circumstances, but the words were sung to his own melody.

Stephen probably earned nothing from *Oh! Susanna*. One account states that he was paid $100.00 for it; this cannot be verified. However, the overwhelming popularity of the song had important effects on Stephen's life. It showed him that he could earn his living as a song-writer—if others could make money from his work, then he could himself. Therefore, he abandoned his effort to make a business man of himself. For business he had neither ability nor inclination—from this time on he devoted himself to writing songs for a livelihood. Moreover he had made a name for himself in the musical world almost over night. The public was eager to purchase other songs by the composer of *Oh! Susanna*, and the leading New York publishing house was glad to make a contract with him for his future compositions.

wed-der it was dry; The sun so hot I froze to def, Su-san-na, don't you cry.

CHORUS

Oh! Su - san - na, do not cry for me; I

come from Al - a - bam - a, Wid my ban - jo on my knee.

2. I had a dream de ud-der night, when eb - ry ting was — still; I thought I saw Su-san-na dear, a com-ing down de — hill, De buck-weat cake was — in her mouf, de tear was in her eye, I says, I'se com - ing from de souf, Su - san-na don't you cry.

Chorus

3d V.

3. I soon will be in New Or - leans, And den I'll look all 'round, And when I find Su - san - na, I'll fall up - on de ground. But if I do not find her, Dis dark-ey'll sure - ly die, And when I'm dead and bur - ied, Su - san - na don't you cry. *Chorus*

ELLEN BAYNE

Published by Firth, Pond & Co., 1854.

This song was very popular in its day, but has been almost forgotten.

1. Soft be thy slum-bers, Rude cares de-part, Vi-sions in num-bers Cheer thy young heart. Dream on while bright hours And fond hopes re-main, Bloom-ing like smil-ing bow'rs For thee, El-len Bayne.

Gen-tle slum-bers o'er thee glide, Dreams of beau-ty round thee bide While I lin-ger

by thy side, Sweet El-len Bayne.

2d V. Dream not in an-guish, Dream not in fear; Love shall not lan-guish; Fond ones are near.

Sleep-ing or wak-ing, In pleas-ure or pain, Warm hearts will beat for thee, Sweet El-len Bayne.
Chorus

3d V. Scenes that have vanish'd Smile on thee now, Pleasures once banished Play round thy brow.

Forms long de-part-ed Greet thee a-gain, Sooth-ing thy dream-ing heart, Sweet El-len Bayne.
Chorus

DOLLY DAY

Published by F. D. Benteen, Baltimore, 1850.

1. I've told you 'bout de banjo, De fid-dle and de bow, Like-wise a-bout de cot-ton field, De shub-ble and de hoe; I've sung a-bout de bul-gine Dat blew de folks a-

2. I like to see de clov-er Dat grows a-bout de lane, I like to see de 'bac-co plant, I like de sug-ar cane; But on de old plan-ta-tion Der's noth-ing half so

3. When de work is o-ver I make de ban-jo play, And while I strike de dul-cem notes, I think of Dol-ly Day. Her form is like a po-sy, De lil-y of de

4. Mas-sa give me mon-ey To buy a peck of corn. I'se guine to mar-ry Dol-ly Day And build my-self a barn; Den when I'm old and fee-ble, And when my head is

way,   And now I'll sing a   lit-tle song A - bout my Dol-ly Day.
gay,   Der's noth-ing dat I   love so much As   my sweet Dol-ly Day.
vale,   Her voice is far de   sweet-est sound Dat floats up - on de gale.
gray,   I'll trab-ble down de   hill of life A - long wid Dol-ly Day.

CHORUS

Oh   Dol - ly   Day   looks   so   gay,   I   run   all   round   and

round   To   hear   her   fair - y   foot-steps play, As   she comes o'er   de ground.

BEAUTIFUL DREAMER

Published by William A. Pond & Co., 1864.

The title page reads: "The last song ever written by Stephen C. Foster." This is an error. There is evidence that the song was written at least six months before Stephen died. After Stephen's death on January 13, 1864, practically every New York publisher who had an unpublished Foster manuscript rushed to get it on the market as "the last work of Stephen Foster." Accordingly there are a number of songs which claim this distinction, making it impossible to determine the actual "last song."

This is certainly the best song that Stephen wrote during his last years. He seems here to have lost himself in his theme as he did in his happier days in Pittsburgh, when he wrote his greatest songs. We can see how genuine was his sentiment in this song when we realize his life and environment at this time. Stephen is evidently seeking an escape from the bitter realities of the Bowery, Broadway, and New York and longs for the happiness of earlier times.

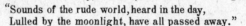

"Sounds of the rude world, heard in the day,
Lulled by the moonlight, have all passed away."

1. Beau-ti-ful dream-er, wake un-to me,___ Star-light and dew-drops are wait-ing for
2. Beau-ti-ful dream-er, out on the sea___ Mer-maids are chaunt-ing the wild lo-re-

thee; _____ Sounds of the rude world heard in the day,___
lie; _____ O-ver the stream-let va-pors are borne,___

Lull'd by the moon-light have all pass'd a-way! _____
Wait-ing to fade at the bright com-ing morn. _____

CAMPTOWN RACES

Published by F. D. Benteen, Baltimore, 1850.

This song is also known as *Gwine to Run All Night.*

go back home wid a pock-et full of tin, Oh! doo-dah-day!
Can't touch bot-tom wid a ten foot pole, Oh! doo-dah-day!
Run-nin' a race wid a shoot-in' star, Oh! doo-dah-day!
keep my mon-ey in an old tow-bag, Oh! doo-dah-day!

CHORUS

Gwine to run all night! Gwine to run all day! I'll

bet my mon-ey on de bob-tail nag, Some-bod-y bet on de bay.

NELLY WAS A LADY

Published by Firth, Pond & Co., 1849.

In connection with the song *My Brudder Gum* there is given an account of royalties received from this song.

Harold Vincent Milligan says: "*Nelly was a Lady* is one of Foster's best melodies; of the utmost simplicity, it speaks with the authentic accents of true and sincere emotion. No amount of elaboration or sophistication could add to the elegiac tenderness of this plaintive little tune, which evokes a mood of gentle sorrow as unerringly today as it did in 1849."

1. Down on de Mis-sis-sip-pi float-ing, Long time I trab-ble on de way,

All night de cot-ton wood a-tot-ing, Sing for my true lub all de day.

Nel - ly was a la - dy   Last night she died,   Toll de bell for lub - ly Nell My

Nel - ly was a la - dy   Last night she died,   Toll de bell for lub - ly Nell My

Nel - ly was a la - dy   Last night she died,   Toll de bell for lub - ly Nell My

Nel - ly was a la - dy   Last night she died,   Toll de bell for lub - ly Nell My

Repeat Chorus

dark Vir - gin - ny bride.

dark Vir - gin - ny bride.

dark Vir - gin - ny bride.

dark Vir - gin - ny bride.

Repeat Chorus

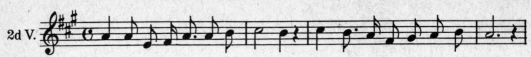

2d V.

Now I'm un-hap-py and I'm weep-ing, Can't tote de cot-ton-wood no more;

Last night, while Nel-ly was a-sleep-ing, Death came a-knock-ing at de door. *Chorus*

3d V.

When I saw my Nel-ly in de morn-ing, Smile till she o-pened up her eyes,

Seemed like de light ob day a-dawn-ing, Jist 'fore de sun be-gin to rise. *Chorus*

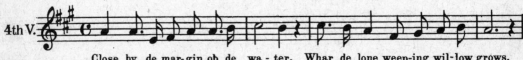

4th V.

Close by de mar-gin ob de wa-ter, Whar de lone weep-ing wil-low grows,

Dar lib'd Vir-gin-ny's lub-ly daugh-ter; Dar she in death may find re-pose. *Chorus*

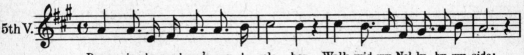

5th V.

Down in de mead-ow 'mong de clo-ber, Walk wid my Nel-ly by my side;

Now all dem hap-py days am o-ber, Fare-well my dark Vir-gin-ny bride. *Chorus*

SWEETLY SHE SLEEPS, MY ALICE FAIR

Published by F. D. Benteen, Baltimore, 1851.

The author of the verses is Charles G. Eastman.

The melody of the song bears a certain resemblance to that of the old Christmas Carol, *It Came Upon a Midnight Clear.*

1. Sweet-ly she sleeps, my Al-ice fair, Her cheek on the pil-low pressed, Sweet-ly she sleeps, while her Sax-on hair, Like sun-light, streams o'er her breast. Hush! Let her sleep! I pray, sweet breeze, Breathe

low on the ma - ple bough! Hush! bright bird, on her win - dow trees! For

sweet - ly she sleep -eth now. Sweet - ly she sleeps, my Al - ice fair, Her

cheek on the pil - low pressed, Sweet -ly she sleeps, while her Sax- on hair, Like

sun-light, streams o'er her breast.

2. Sweet-ly she sleeps, my Al-ice fair, Her cheek like the first May rose,—

Sweet-ly she sleeps, and all her care Is for-got-ten in soft re-pose.

Hush! though the ear-liest beams of light Their wings in the blue sea

dip, Let her sleep, I pray, while her dreams are bright, And a

ad lib.

smile is a-bout her lip.___ Sweet-ly she sleeps, my

Al - ice fair, Her cheek on the pil - low pressed,___

Sweet-ly she sleeps, while her Sax-on hair, Like sun-light, streams o'er her breast.

KATY BELL

Published by S. T. Gordon, 1863.

A sentimental ballad written by George Cooper. Music composed by Stephen C. Foster.

1. Go - ing down the sha - dy dell, Where the hon - ey - suck - les grow,
2. All the flow - ers in the dell Seem'd to own her for their queen,
3. Long I wait - ed in the dell, Where the hon - ey - suck - les grow,

I met love - ly Ka - ty Bell With her dim - pled cheeks a - glow.
Bright and peer - less Ka - ty Bell, Fair - er flow'r was nev - er seen.
Wait - ed for sweet Ka - ty Bell, Till the sun was sink - ing low.

Oh! the beau - ties of her face, As she flit - ted by a - pace,
How I loved the ver - y ground, O - ver which she'd light - ly bound,
And be - fore I left her side, In the qui - et e - ven- tide

With a step of fair - y grace. My poor words can nev - er tell.
With her sun - ny ring - lets crown'd, I can nev - er, nev - er tell.
I had won her for my bride, Won my bon - ny Ka - ty Bell.

CHORUS (Unison or four parts)

Ka - ty Bell lives in the dell, How I love her none can tell.

LAURA LEE

Published by F. D. Benteen, Baltimore, 1851.

1. Why has thy mer-ry face
2. Far from all pleas-ure torn,
3. When will thy win-ning voice

Gone from my side,
Sad and a - lone,
Breathe on mine ear?

Leav - ing each cher-ished place
How doth my spir - it mourn
When will my heart re -joice,

Cheer - less and
While thou art
Find - ing thee

void?
gone!
near?

Why has the hap - py dream,
How like a des - ert isle
When will we roam the plain,

Blend - ed with thee,
Earth seems to me,
Joy - ous and free,

OLD MEMORIES

Published by Firth, Pond & Co., 1853.

hap-py days can nev-er re-turn! Say not those hap-py days can
hap-py days can nev-er re-turn! Say not those hap-py days can

nev-er re-turn!
nev-er re-turn!

PARTHENIA TO INGOMAR

Published by Firth, Pond & Co., 1859.

Words written by William Henry McCarthy.

McCarthy was evidently a Pittsburgh friend of Stephen. They collaborated on three songs, and Stephen's account book shows royalties received on these three songs and his sharing of the royalties with McCarthy.

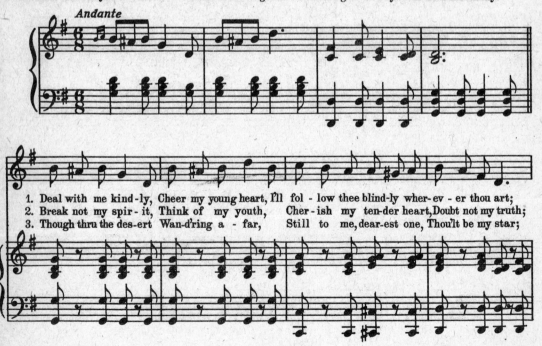

Andante

1. Deal with me kind-ly, Cheer my young heart, I'll fol-low thee blind-ly wher-ev-er thou art;
2. Break not my spir-it, Think of my youth, Cher-ish my ten-der heart, Doubt not my truth;
3. Though thru the des-ert Wan-d'ring a-far, Still to me, dear-est one, Thou'lt be my star;

Deep in the moun-tain, Far from my home, I'll fol-low thy path wher-ev-er thou'lt roam.
Friends may de-sert thee, Sor-rows may come, But still in this soul Thine im-age will bloom.
Sun-light or moon-light O'er us may shine, Yet liv-ing on love, I'll ev-er be thine.

Thy way shall still be mine, My heart shall still be thine;
Thy hopes with thee I'll share, Thy wants shall be my care;
Thy hand shall be my guard, Thy voice shall be my word;

Deal with me kind - ly, Cheer my young heart, I'll fol - low thee blind - ly And
Deal with me kind - ly, Cheer my young heart, I'll fol - low thee blind - ly And
Deal with me kind - ly, Cheer my young heart, I'll fol - low thee blind - ly And

rit.

nev - er de - part.
nev - er de - part.
nev - er de - part.

a tempo

p

UNDER THE WILLOW SHE'S SLEEPING

Publishished by Firth, Pond & Co., 1860.

1. Un-der the wil-low she's laid with care, (Sang a lone moth-er while weep-ing,)
2. Un-der the wil-low no songs are heard, Near where my dar-ling lies dream-ing;
3. Un-der the wil-low by night and day, Sor-row-ing ev-er I pon-der;
4. Un-der the wil-low I breathe a prayer, Long-ing to lin-ger for-ev-er

Un-der the wil-low with gold-en hair, My lit-tle one's qui-et-ly sleep-ing.
Nought but the voice of some far-off bird Where life and its pleas-ures are beam-ing.
Free from its shad-ow-y, gloom-y ray, Ah! nev-er a-gain can she wan-der.
Near to my an-gel with gold-en hair, In lands where there's sor-row-ing nev-er.

Fair, fair, and gold-en hair; (Sang a lone moth-er while weep-ing,)

Fair, fair, and gold-en hair; (Sang a lone moth-er while weep-ing,)

Fair, fair, and gold-en hair; Un-der the wil-low she's sleep-ing.

Fair, fair, and gold-en hair; Un-der the wil-low she's sleep-ing.

THE GLENDY BURK

Published by Firth, Pond & Co., 1860.

The Mississippi River steamboat "Glendy Burke" inspired this lively song. The "Glendy Burke" was built at New Albany, Indiana, in 1851, and was considered a magnificent boat. She was named after a New Orleans banker and philanthropist. (Foster drops the "e" from "Burke" in his song.)

1. De Glen-dy Burk is a might-y fast boat, Wid a might-y fast cap-tain too; He sits up dah on de hur-ri-cane roof And he keeps his eye on de

crew.   I   can't stay here, for dey work too hard; I'm bound   to leave dis

town;   I'll   take my duds and tote 'em on my back When de Glen-dy Burk comes down.

CHORUS (All Voices)

Ho!   for Lou'- si - an - a!   I'm bound   to leave dis   town; I'll   take my duds and

tote 'em on my back When de Glen-dy Burk comes down.

SOME FOLKS

1. Some folks like to sigh, Some folks do, some folks do;
2. Some folks fear to smile, Some folks do, some folks do;
3. Some folks fret and scold, Some folks do, some folks do; They'll
4. Some folks get gray hairs, Some folks do, some folks do;
5. Some folks toil and save, Some folks do, some folks do, To

Some folks long to die, But that's not me nor you.
Oth - ers laugh through guile, But that's not me nor you.
soon be dead and cold, But that's not me nor you.
Brood-ing o'er their cares, But that's not me nor you.
buy them-selves a grave, But that's not me nor you.

CHORUS *Vivace*

Long live the mer-ry, mer-ry heart That laughs by night and day, Like the Queen of Mirth, No mat-ter what some folks say.

TITLE INDEX

MONUMENT TO STEPHEN FOSTER
Fargo, Georgia
Dedicated October 27, 1928
Donated by Charles J. Haden of Atlanta, Georgia